Sprouting!

a guide to the ultimate superfood

Deborah Fowler

First published in 2006 by Truran, Croft Prince, Mount Hawke,
Truro, Cornwall TR4 8EE
www.Truranbooks.co.uk
Truran is an imprint of Truran Books Ltd

Reprinted 2007

Cover image © Clive Thorp

ISBN **978 185022 211 8**

Printed and bound in Cornwall by R Booth Ltd,
Antron Hill, Mabe, Penryn, Cornwall TR10 9HH

Special thanks as always to Jo Pearce for turning my ramblings
into a readable manuscript, to Sally Gilbert and Charlie Fowler
for couriering between us, and to my family for their
ongoing encouragement.

Contents

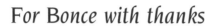

For Bonce with thanks

Foreword

Life has become very complicated. I wonder how many of us are really looking forward with much confidence and enthusiasm to the 21st century. With wars, terrorism and global warming to contend with, we tend to seek comfort in familiar things. Nature has always provided that – a beautiful view, the changing seasons, the taste of the first blackberry have always lifted the spirits – but things are not what they seem any more. The air we breathe, the water we drink, the food we eat often carry hidden ingredients, ingredients that pollute and poison, taint and destroy, enemies which only show themselves in the form of the appalling increases in cancer, allergies and a whole range of new modern diseases.

I am so sorry to introduce a book with so much doom and gloom, but this is where it ends ... promise, from now on we will be positive! Even in the regimented state in which we now find ourselves living, we can take control of our own lives. Work permitting, we can choose to live in an environment which is not too heavily polluted. We can grow our own vegetables, rear our own chickens, if we have the land. If we have access to a local farm shop and the income available to shop there, we can radically improve our health by the quality of food we eat. Simple solutions, then? No, of course not, there are too many 'ifs'. For many of us, these options are just not possible, impractical and well beyond our resources. However, there is a way to really help you and your family keep, not just healthy, but packed full of all the necessary vitamins, minerals, enzymes and trace elements that today are missing from most people's diets. By making your kitchen also your garden, for just a few pence a day and a couple of minutes of your time, you can quite literally change your life. It is an option available to everyone, however tight your budget, however demanding your job. A ridiculous claim?   No – sprouted seeds and beans can give you every nutrient you need for healthy living and quite literally put you back in charge of your life.

Deborah Fowler
Cornwall

Chapter 1
What are Sprouts?

Somewhere along the evolutionary path, we took a wrong turning. Grains are the staple diet of almost the entire population of the world in one form or another. However, in order for grains to be digestible, they are usually boiled up, like oats or rice, or ground down and baked into bread. There is an apparently good reason for this. Grains, pulses and seeds, eaten raw, are very hard to digest and cause a great deal of discomfort if we try to do so. However, the act of cooking the grains to make them digestible also destroys all the plant enzymes and it is this complete lack of enzymes in much of the food we eat today which is causing so many health problems. Instead of cooking, if the seed or bean is sprouted and then eaten raw, not only is it digestible, it is converted, magically, into what can only be described as perfect food.

At the point of germination a miracle occurs. The enzymes within the seed or bean kick-start the nutrients which are stored there in an inert form. The result can only be described, as a nutritional superfood. A sprout is a baby at a stage between being a seed and being a plant. In those first few days of life, the sprout is not capable of feeding itself (ie developing a root structure) and nor does it need to do so because it contains within the seed or bean the perfect nutritional mix to sustain itself. It contains, if you like, the plant equivalent of mother's milk. When trying to describe what germination does to a seed or bean, I always liken it to a rocket going to the moon. As the rocket leaves the launch pad, it is packed full of fuel to take it all the way on its long journey. It is also at maximum thrust to get it off the ground, through the atmosphere and into space – in other words at that moment of launch, it is at its most powerful. This is exactly the state of a sprouting seed at the point of germination. It has all the fuel on board to turn it into a fully grown plant and it is also packed full of the energy ready to take it on its journey. At the point of germination, proteins, vitamins, minerals, enzymes and trace elements within the seed multiply between three and twelve hundred per cent. You will understand why I call it a miracle.

Enzymes

Enzymes are rather lacking in good publicity. Everyone knows the importance of vitamins and minerals in a diet, but enzymes are rarely mentioned. Yet enzymes have a vital role to play in our well being, in fact they are probably the most important component in our food. Every living thing contains enzymes. We have our own store of them and the trick is not to deplete our store too much. We can achieve this by eating enzyme-rich food, but the problem is that in today's modern diet, many of the foods we eat are entirely without enzymes because they are easily destroyed in cooking. Temperatures as low as 48C can destroy them, so every time we eat a cooked meal, devoid of any fresh raw food, we deplete our own enzyme store.

So, what role do enzymes play in our life? They control

nearly every function of our bodies. They help us digest the food we eat, they assist in the elimination of toxins and they support the immune system. They are also extremely important for longevity. Youthfulness is linked, without doubt, to the state of our enzyme reserves. If we eat plenty of fresh, raw food, packed with nutrients, then we do not draw too heavily on our own enzymes and they in turn will keep a bounce in our step. The more cooked food we eat, the more of our own reserves we squander, the quicker the ageing process. The extraordinary thing about eating enzyme-rich raw food is that, even after years of abuse, the body will react almost immediately and dramatically to a diet of raw or mainly raw fruit and vegetables. It is so much more satisfactory than a conventional diet. If you introduce raw food into your diet, yes, you will lose weight, but more importantly, you will feel so much better and have much more energy, so quickly, that you will need little convincing to continue with it. It is just a question of taking that first step.

Chlorophyll

Like enzymes, chlorophyll does not have a particularly good press. Chlorophyll is the green pigment in plants, it is condensed solar energy, the lifeblood of a plant and has been described, rather well I think, as 'liquid sunshine'. So what does chlorophyll do? It is a great protector against toxins and carcinogens, it is anti-inflammatory, it rejuvenates the liver, it is antibacterial, heals, restores and improves skin and hair, aids arthritis, regulates the menstrual cycle and is packed full of energy.

With a list of attributes like these, you can see why chlorophyll is so important. The best source of chlorophyll is wheatgrass which is why I have devoted an entire chapter to the subject (See Chapter 4) but all sprouted seeds and beans contain an abundance of chlorophyll. For people who spend a lot of time indoors, either because of their place of work, or because they live in a city or are housebound, chlorophyll is vital for maintaining good health. So, I hear you ask, you have made a case for eating raw vegetables but why sprouting seeds and beans? Why don't I just go to my local supermarket and buy some salad stuff, eat that and save myself a lot of trouble?

The answer is because you can't trust supermarket quality and freshness and because it can never be so effective as growing your own sprouts. Mass market agriculture robs the soil of its natural minerals and there are still a lot of very nasty synthetic fertilisers and insecticides out there. Salad stuff is particularly vulnerable to all sorts of bugs and is therefore subject to every trick in the book in order to get it to the supermarket shelf in an apparently healthy state. Food you grow yourself, preferably washed in rain water, is food upon which you can rely.

More importantly still, of course, is that the nutritional value of a lettuce leaf cannot even be compared with that of a newly sprouted seed for all the reasons I have explained. Sprouting seeds and beans are so powerful that you need to eat only 4–5ozs (about 100g) a day, to have all the vitamins, minerals, trace elements and enzymes you need for healthy living. They are so versatile – put your sprouting seeds or beans in sandwiches, salads, in juices, add them at the last moment to cooked dishes and sauces. At the end of this book you will find a selection of recipes.

Growing sprouts is easy, as you will see. Eating them is, too!

Chapter 2
Sprouting seeds and their properties

I n this chapter I have listed the main seeds for sprouting in alphabetical order, together with their properties and information on soaking and sprouting times.

Of course, you can sprout almost any seed to eat as a baby plant but I have concentrated here on those which are the most nutritious and also the easiest to sprout. With our busy lives to consider, I am aware of the importance of making the whole sprouting process as quick and easy for you as possible.

Alfalfa Seeds

Soaking time: 4–6 hours
Sprouting time: 4 days
Uses: in salads, sandwiches, as a finger food,
in juices, in bread, as a garnish

Alfalfa means the "father of all foods" in Arabic: it contains just about everything the body needs for survival. Alfalfa rejuvenates the system, detoxifies and enriches the liver, assists in weight loss, purifies the blood, aids digestion and acts a general tonic. It contains all known vitamins and also calcium, magnesium, potassium, iron, selenium and zinc. It is said that if one was stuck in a nuclear bunker for three months, one could live on alfalfa and water alone and come out with all organs functioning well. It is a true superfood. In ancient times, alfalfa was used to fight illness and build strength. In 1935, researchers found vitamin K, which aids blood clotting, in alfalfa. This prompted further research, causing amazement when the extraordinarily high level of vitamins and minerals was found. It was discovered that eating alfalfa causes a dramatic reduction in cholesterol levels. It is easy to sprout. Often you see it for sale fresh in the chill cabinet as a rather insipid white sprout. I prefer to see it 'greened up'. By exposing the seeds to indirect sunlight for the last couple of days of growth, you will greatly increase the chlorophyll content in your alfalfa sprouts.

Broccoli Seeds

Soaking time: 4–6 hours
Sprouting time: 3 days
Uses: in salads, sandwiches, juices and finger food

Broccoli sprouts are a powerful anti-oxidant, providing considerable support to the immune system. Researchers at the University of Texas Cancer Center have found that sprouting broccoli seriously inhibits the growth of cancer cells (See Chapter Seven). Broccoli sprouts are wonderful to eat in the winter when you feel run down and are always catching colds and bugs. Good helpings of broccoli sprouts will give you the boost you need, a genuine tonic. They are vitamin-rich and slightly peppery to taste.

Fenugreek Seeds

Soaking time: 8 hours
Sprouting time: 2–3 days
Uses: add to curries as a garnish or fold into a curry
at the end of cooking.
Also add to salads, juices and bread-making for a spicy taste

Fenugreek is one of mankind's oldest medicinal plants. It was much prized by the ancient Egyptians, Greeks and Romans, It is also used in Chinese medicine.

Modern clinical studies show that fenugreek has cholesterol-lowering and blood glucose-lowering properties. Significant lowering of cholesterol levels have been recorded in patients eating 250g per day, and for diabetics, eating 500g per day is proving helpful, not only with regard to blood sugar levels, but also with the side effects of diabetes.

Fenugreek has been known for thousands of years as a tonic after illness or when tired or run down. Fenugreek aids detoxification of the liver, it is anti-inflammatory, an anti-oxidant, helps prevent cell damage caused by free radicals, reduces and controls blood pressure, it is anti-spasmodic, eases symptoms of arthritis and the menopause and encourages breast milk. Monks in the Middle Ages used fenugreek to treat blood poisoning and it is cultivated in the Arab world where it is traditionally used to stimulate the appetite.

Flax Seeds (Linseed)

Soaking time: Ten minutes
Sprouting time: 4 days
Uses: in salads, sandwiches, fruit juice
and add to stir fries at the end of cooking

Flax is a major source of Omega 3. Research in Germany concludes that flax stimulates the immune system, inhibits the growth of cancer cells and controls both cholesterol and hypertension. The sprouted seed also acts like psyllium to help cleanse the intestinal tract. Flax is a wonderfully nutritious seed but not the easiest to sprout because it becomes gelatinous when soaked and the resultant "goo" makes it difficult for the seed to sprout. The best way to sprout flax is to include it with a good tempered sprouting seed such as alfalfa or red clover. Techniques for sprouting will be covered in Chapters 5 and 6 but it is worth mentioning here that one should mix flax in a ratio of one dessert spoon of flax to four of alfalfa or red clover for best results.

Garlic Chive Seeds

Soaking time: 8 *hours*
Sprouting time: 4 *days*
Uses: *add to salads and sandwiches, garnish cooked dishes*
including casseroles, soups and eggs

They say that the pyramids were built on garlic – feeding the labourers large quantities kept them fit and strong. Garlic has long held a reputation for its antibiotic qualities, indeed tests on raw garlic have shown that it can be more powerful than penicillin. Garlic is antiseptic, anti-viral, anti-fungal, anti-spasmodic and has a justifiable reputation for lowering blood pressure and helping prevent the formation of dangerous blood clots. It also aids in the lowering of cholesterol and is famously an excellent treatment for the common cold. No wonder those pyramids are so impressive!

Unless you are a serious Frenchman, eating raw garlic is not something that comes easily due to the overpowering odour and the resultant catastrophic effects on your love life! However a sprouted garlic chive is virtually odour free and is a very palatable way of acquiring this marvellous plant's magic medicine.

Mustard Seeds

Soaking time: 8 hours
Sprouting time: 4 days
Uses: in salads, sandwiches, add to Mexican dishes
when cooked, also soups and curries

For sprouters, black mustard seed is the one to go for, rather than yellow, for yellow tends to be gelatinous and therefore much harder to germinate. Black, by contrast, is really very easy-going and good tempered. Mustard is very effective in treating sinus congestion. It contains vitamins A and C, most minerals and chlorophyll. Obviously the flavour of mustard sprouts is strong so it is best to mix them with other sprouting seeds. They work very well with both alfalfa and red clover in particular as they take about the same amount of time to sprout. Not only do they taste good together, but also look good.

Quinoa (pronounced Keen-wa)
The Ancient Grain

Soaking time: 8 hours
Sprouting time: 1 day
Uses: in salads, sandwiches, as a garnish, in bread making

This wonderful tasty and traditional food was grown by the Incas on terraces, on the Andes Mountains in Peru, in Bolivia and in Chile where it is still grown today. The Incas ground it into flour for bread and used its leaves for vegetables. They used its stalks for fuel and used the water from which they soaked the grain as a soap. You can buy quinoa flour, which makes excellent bread and is particularly helpful for people with wheat allergies. It is also very tasty cooked quickly (about 15 minutes) to use instead of rice. Quinoa is vitamin-rich in the B vitamins and also vitamin E, plus amino acids. It also has more protein than any other grain with an average of 16.2 per cent which means it is the perfect seed for vegetarians, vegans and also, of course, dieters. Quinoa sprouts very quickly, within a day, and should be eaten as soon as possible. As a young sprout it is sweet and makes an excellent snack, but if it is allowed to grow too long, it becomes bitter, fibrous and rots easily.

Red Clover Seeds

Soaking time: 4 *hours*
Sprouting time: 4 *days*
Uses: in salads, sandwiches, juices and as finger food

Herbalist Jethro Kloss described red clover as 'one of God's greatest blessings to man'. Red clover contains vitamins A and C, valuable trace elements and has a very high mineral content which has given it a reputation for promoting fertility and restoring the hormonal balance, particularly during the menopause. Red clover also has a reputation as a blood cleanser, for helping settle the stomach, improving weak nerves and increasing energy levels. It also helps alkalise the body and promote detoxification. It is an extremely easy sprout to grow and pleasant-tasting, if a little bland.

Sesame Seeds

Soaking time: 10 *minutes*
Sprouting time: 4 *days*
Uses: *add to yoghurt, cheese, breads and breakfast cereal*

Zinc is a mineral which is very often absent in the modern diet and the need for zinc increases during times of stress. Sesame seed is rich in zinc and also calcium, magnesium, phosphorous and vitamins B, D and E. Sesame seeds are not the easiest to sprout and like flax are best sprouted with alfalfa or red clover to absorb some of the glutinous quality of the seeds. Sprout on the basis of four alfalfa or red clover to one portion of sesame seeds (See Chapter 5).

White Radish

Soaking time: 8 hours
Sprouting time: 3 days
Uses: in salads, sandwiches, juices, add to dressings and chop into soups, curries and in Mexican foods as a garnish

White radish sprouts are best known as an expectorant. They clear mucus from the respiratory tract and therefore are wonderful for ailments such as colds, sinus congestion, bronchitis, whooping cough and are also helpful in the treatment of asthma. White radish is also an effective diuretic, restoring troubles of the urinary tract, bladder and kidneys and is good for the entire digestive system. It is the best detox sprout. White radish sprouts contain potassium, vitamin C and chlorophyll and have a hot, spicy taste – hotter, in fact, than the fully grown radish, the flavour being more concentrated.

Pumpkin and Sunflower Seeds

Soaking time: 12 hours
Sprouting time: None
Uses: In salads, curries, chilli or just munch them

Two Unsprouted Seeds

I have not included these two seeds for sprouting because they don't (sprout, I mean) – at least not easily! Both seeds are packed full of vitamins, minerals and trace elements and are absolutely delicious if eaten immediately after soaking. However, it is difficult to get them to sprout properly. The seeds swell up after twelve hours of soaking and are then sweet, delicious and nutritious. Both seeds are best eaten shortly after soaking and should be kept in the fridge as they rot very easily. In both cases eat within two days of soaking. Despite the fact that both seeds are very volatile, it is worth persevering with them because they are so valuable nutritionally.

Pumpkin seeds contain vitamin E, amino acids, essential fatty acids, phosphorous, iron and zinc.

Sunflower seeds are almost a complete food. They are rich in the B vitamins including B15, vitamin E, amino acids, calcium, phosphorous, iron, magnesium and potassium.

Chapter 3
Sprouting Beans and their Properties

Sprouting beans tends to be a quicker and easier process than sprouting seeds so long as you do not leave them sitting in a puddle – they rot if not properly drained. For many, the concept of eating beans is out of the question because they see them as being the cause of flatulence and indigestion. This does not apply to sprouting beans. Beans that are so indigestible in the unsprouted state become very easy on the digestive system once sprouted. Indeed, sprouted beans can be given to the most vulnerable of digestive systems. Beans are wonderful. They lower cholesterol and blood pressure, they carry cancer blocking substances, they are packed full of protein and a wide range of nutrients. Any of the beans I have listed can put together to make a wonderful bean salad which is deliciously filling without being fattening – beans are a wonderful aid to slimming and vital for good nutrition. It is important that vegetarians make beans a major part of their diet – particularly aduki beans which are so rich in protein.

Remember the rhyme:
'Beans, beans are good for the heart, the more you eat, the more you fart!'
Sprouted beans are certainly responsible for the former attribute, but mercifully, not the latter!

Aduki Beans

Soaking time: 24 hours.
Sprouting time: 2 days
*Uses: in salads, sandwiches, add to stir fries when cooking is
finished, soups and sprout loaves*

Aduki are a native of Japan and have a sweet, slightly nutty taste. They are a red bean, lighter in colour but not unsimilar in shape to a kidney bean. However, unlike kidney beans, they can be eaten raw, and are absolutely delicious. They are a rich source of vitamin C, iron and especially protein. They are a good tonic and particularly useful for vegans and vegetarians as part of their staple diet because of the rich protein content. They are easy to grow and have a good shelf-life of at least five or six days in the fridge once sprouted.

Black Eyed Beans

Soaking time: 24 hours
Sprouting time: 2 days
Uses: add to stir fries and oriental dishes at the end of cooking,
sprout loaves and salads

B lack eyed beans have a pleasant gentle flavour. They are a good source of vitamins A, B3, B5, C and amino acids, magnesium, potassium, iron, calcium, phosphorous and zinc. They are easy and quick to grow. A particularly attractive bean to use in stir-frys – its dark colour gives a slightly exotic look to a dish.

Chickpeas

Soaking time: 8 hours
Sprouting time: 2 days
Uses: for hummus, sprouted bread, salads and casseroles

Chickpeas contain vitamins A and C, amino acids, carbohydrates, fibre, calcium, magnesium and potassium. Unsprouted, even after cooking, chickpeas can be indigestible. However, when sprouted, the active enzymes ensure that the bean can be eaten raw without any discomfort. For this reason, any traditional dishes you may consider making are best made with sprouted chickpeas. I am thinking particularly of hummus, but also sprout loaves and casseroles. Chickpeas should be eaten soon after sprouting. Even when kept in the fridge, they have a very short shelf-life (2 days at best). Out of the fridge they tend to go slimy, in the fridge they tend to dry out, so do not sprout too many at a time and eat them as soon as they are harvested. Chickpeas are a useful aid for reducing cholesterol.

Green Peas

Soaking time: 12 hours
Sprouting time: 2 days
Uses: in salads, sandwiches, as a finger food,
add to soups just before serving

Green peas have the delicious flavour of freshly picked garden peas. They are very nutritious and are a good source of carbohydrates, protein and fibre, plus vitamin A, the B vitamins, folic acid, calcium, magnesium, phosphorous and potassium. Like chickpeas, however, they do have a very short shelf life, when sprouted, and are best eaten straight away rather than stored.

Lentils

Soaking time: 12 hours
Sprouting time: 2 days
Uses: in salads, sprouting bread, fold into casseroles
and soups after cooking

Lentils, both green and brown, are an extremely good source of vitamin C. They are also rich in iron and amino acids and are good for both the lowering of cholesterol and blood pressure. They also have a high protein content, indeed more so than red meat, but without, of course, the fat content. Lentils nourish the kidneys and adrenaline glands and help produce antibodies to ward off infection. Both green and brown lentils are easy to sprout, they have a mild nutty taste, and look good in bean salads. Lentils store well, too, they should be fine in the fridge for up to a week.

Mung Beans

Soaking time: 24 hours
Sprouting time: 2 days
Uses: in salads, sandwiches, add to stir fries, sprouting bread, in juices
and use as a finger food

Mung beans are absolutely delicious, tasting rather like young peas straight from the pod and therefore children love them. They are a wonderful blood and liver cleanser and are soothing to the digestive system. As with most beans, mung beans aid in clearing the dangerous LDL cholesterol in the blood and the bean's fibre content also helps lower blood pressure. Mung are high in amino acids, iron, potassium and vitamins A, C and E and they are also a great energy boost. They are excellent to use in any form of detox programme and are very easy to sprout. Above all, they are a serious energy boost – which most of us could do with from time to time! Truly wonderful, tasting good, doing you good and so easy to sprout.

Chapter 4
Wheatgrass

I feel positively evangelistic about wheatgrass. Wheatgrass juice offers just about perfect nutrition. It is so easy to grow and so cheap and from my experience, once you start juicing and drinking wheatgrass, the effects are almost instantaneous. Think about it – grass is the food which maintains the earth's herbivores. Herbivores are strong, healthy, bursting with energy and endurance and for most of them, grass is all they eat. Grass is, in fact, the only food which is capable of maintaining an herbivorous animal in good health throughout its life.

We, too, can benefit hugely from eating this perfect food but there is one big problem – unlike cows, we do not have enough stomachs to digest wheatgrass! In order for us to eat it, we have to juice it. You can chop a few pieces of wheatgrass into a salad – rather like you would chives, but the quantity you eat this way will have little effect. Juicing is the only viable means of consuming fresh wheatgrass in sufficient quantities to do you good.

It was research carried out by Doctor Ann Wigmore who first alerted the world to the power of wheatgrass juice. In her book she cites many cases of people with incurable illnesses who have been restored to health following a course of wheatgrass juice. I am not a doctor, and while I have been told some truly amazing stories concerning the power of wheatgrass, I do not have the qualifications or authority to present you with any such cases. However I do know how wheatgrass makes my family, my friends, my staff and my customers feel, not to mention me, too! Making wheatgrass a part of your daily living is a life-changing experience.

Wheatgrass heals, rejuvenates, energises and nourishes

Wheatgrass **heals** because it is a very powerful antioxidant. Wheatgrass **rejuvenates** because the properties contained within wheatgrass, particularly chlorophyll, help restore the body and protect it against the effects of ageing. Dr Ann Wigmore reported that her hair returned to its natural colour rather than grey after she included wheatgrass in her diet, and certainly the condition of hair and skin improves enormously as does the elasticity of joints when taking wheatgrass regularly.

Wheatgrass **energises** – it gives a terrific energy boost and for that reason it is best taken in the mornings with breakfast. An interesting thing happened to me a few months ago. I was exhibiting our sprouting seeds at Badminton Horse Trials, which is a four day show. The weather was very hot and I decided not to demonstrate juicing wheatgrass on the stand, which is what I normally do, because I thought the conditions would make it too difficult so far from home. What I had forgotten to think about was what I was going to do without my own daily wheatgrass shot. By day three I was absolutely exhausted – I felt like Popeye without his spinach! It made me realise just how much energy wheatgrass was giving me on a daily basis.

Wheatgrass **nourishes** – wheatgrass contains pretty much every known vitamin, mineral, trace element, enzymes and chlorophyll. It is perfect nutrition.

DOSAGE: *Take between 30ml and 60ml daily but not more than 90ml in any one day.*

There are a number of wheatgrass products on the market – powders, capsules and some juices and tinctures which contain a cocktail of ingredients, including wheatgrass. Some of the powders and capsules can be very effective nutritionally but even though claims are made that it is possible to air-dry the powders and retain live enzymes, it is very hard to see how this works. To be honest, many of the 'wheatgrass cocktails' on the market at the moment are of very little value at all because wheatgrass does not take kindly to being mixed with anything else, nor kept for any length of time. For guaranteed nutrition with all the benefits afforded by both live enzymes and chlorophyll, it is best to grow wheatgrass yourself and juice it on a daily basis. It is surprisingly easy once you establish a routine.

Growing Methods

Wheatgrass should be grown in ordinary seed trays which you can purchase from any garden centre. For absolute optimum nutrition, it is best to grow wheatgrass in organic compost but this method is only really viable if you have a greenhouse or conservatory.

Trying to cope with soil in the kitchen is neither easy nor sensible. As a less messy, but equally viable alternative, you can either grow wheatgrass on organic garden fleece (again easily obtainable from a garden centre) or hydroponically – that is growing the wheatgrass in a seed tray on nothing at all and relying on daily watering alone to sustain its growth.

I grow wheatgrass commercially for juice bars and have looked at all three methods. Juice bars, like the domestic kitchen, cannot cope with soil. Most juice bars are fairly small and need to keep their surfaces clean and clear so I supply them with wheatgrass grown hydroponically and research indicates that there is no significant difference in nutritional value from wheatgrass grown on compost. It is interesting that Dr Ann Wigmore, the founder of the whole wheatgrass movement, only ever grew her wheatgrass on compost. Many growers who worked for her, and have, since her death, started businesses of their own, are using the hydroponic method as research has now indicated that it does not greatly affect the value of the product. After all, sprouts are grown hydroponically and wheatgrass is really just a big sprout.

Everyone has different methods for growing wheatgrass. I can only tell you mine which does work very well.

Regardless of whether you are using fleece, organic compost or nothing at all, you need to purchase organic wheatgrain, preferably from a health food shop with a good reputation – you don't want old grain which has been sitting on a shelf for years. One hundred and fifty grams of unsprouted wheat is the right amount to put on a single seed tray. First soak your wheatgrain for approximately 8–10 hours. If it suits you to do your soaking overnight, that is fine, but do not leave the grain soaking for any longer than 12 hours. Rinse the wheatgrain very thoroughly through a colander until the water draining through is clear in colour. Then return the wheatgrain to the container in which you soaked it. Cover it and allow it to sprout for another 24 hours, washing it through the colander twice more during that period.

After 24 hours, you will see that the wheatgrain casing is starting to break and the sprout is beginning to appear. At this point it is ready to put onto the seed tray. If you are using the soil method, lay the grain evenly on the soil and put only a very fine sprinkle of compost on top of it. If you are using garden fleece then thoroughly soak the fleece, lay the grain on top of it and water again. If you are using the hydroponic method you might well find it better to let the wheatgrass sprout for another 12 hours in the soaking container so it is larger and does not fall through the holes in the seed tray. If you do this, remember to rinse them again. Once the seeds are in their tray and watered in, I always put the whole tray in a plastic bag for 24 hours and this ensures that germination is completed. Thereafter it is simply a question of watering the wheatgrass daily. However, if you are growing it hydroponically and the weather is really hot, you would be wise to water twice a day. Wheatgrass trays should not be placed in direct sunlight though they do need plenty of light in order to ensure they develop enough chlorophyll. Try and make their environment as airy as possible.

The grass will take about nine days to reach the stage of

maturity when it is ready for juicing. It is not an exact science. You are looking for a growth of about 6–10 inches. Sometimes during the growing process, the grass will establish a mould at its base around the grain. The mould is grey and white in colour and not very attractive but, in fact, it will not affect the quality of the grass. If mould does appear, rinse it off rigorously during the daily watering process by using a spray or hose to really wash it away. Mould only tends to appear in the summer when the weather is particularly humid.

Juicing

U nfortunately, wheatgrass cannot be juiced in a conventional juicer because the fibre in the grass quickly jams up the mechanism, leading eventually to the burning out of the motor – not a good idea! There are a number of juicers on the market at the moment quite specifically for wheatgrass. If you have a large family then it is probably worth investing in an electric juicer but having said that, the hand juicers, at a fraction of the price, work very well. In fact, purists maintain that wheatgrass should only be juiced by hand because the electric juicers tend to froth up the juice a little, which reduces its nutritional value. There is little evidence to support this theory – I think it might be a case of 'juicer envy'! Wheatgrass juice should be drunk on a daily basis and that means it should be juiced on a daily basis, too. While you can store it in the fridge for a few hours, the best way to take wheatgrass is to simply juice it and drink it.

In the early days of taking wheatgrass, you may find the sweet distinctive flavour of the grass not particularly palatable, in which case you can mix it with fruit juice, provided you drink it immediately. Most people say that after a week or two they become used to the taste of the juice and even grow to quite like it! Certainly, my own experience is that I frankly hated the taste initially and made a big fuss about taking it each morning. Now I never think about it – just knock it back.

The yield from a seed tray does vary. On the whole, wheatgrass grown on soil will produce a bigger yield. If you allow your grass to grow to about 20–23cm (8–9 in) in height then you should obtain 250ml from a seed tray – about a weeks worth of juice for one person. Therefore, if you start your second seed tray when germination is completed on the first one, you will always have grass available for juicing.

One final point on the difference between hydroponic growing and growing on soil – the flavour of grass grown on soil will prove to be slightly stronger than grass grown hydroponically. This could be said to be an advantage for the hydroponic system!

So why not have a go – wheatgrass truly is nature's finest medicine.

Chapter 5
Growing and Growing Apparatus

There are various different methods of growing sprouting seeds and beans which I will outline in detail in this chapter. However, there are a few golden rules which apply to sprouting irrespective of the method you use. These are as follows:

Golden Rules of Sprouting

1 View what you do to sprouts as a washing process rather than a watering process. Whatever method you use, vigorously wash the sprouts and then thoroughly drain them. Never, ever leave them sitting with wet feet. If they are left in a puddle, the sprouts will develop mould and a very nasty smell.

2 Do not sprout too many seeds at once. Seeds packed in too tightly together are difficult to wash properly which again will lead to mould. Also, tightly packed sprouts, like tightly packed people, are not happy. To grow well, sprouts need light and air. When you first start sprouting, it is amazing to see just how much growth develops from so few seeds. I recommend a flat

dessertspoon of seeds per crop as being right for a family of 2–4. Little and often is the best way to sprout.

3 Never put sprouts in the path of direct heat, either by placing them on a sunny windowsill, on a radiator, or in an airing cupboard. Sprouts like the same climate conditions that you like to live in – warm but not too hot, no draughts; pleasant, light, airy conditions. Sprouting beans do not need light but neither must they be kept in the dark. Both seeds and beans are pretty good tempered about where you keep them, provided the temperature is not too extreme or variable.

4 Regularity – for best results, you need to get into a routine. Like most living things, sprouts thrive on routine. Maybe when you get up in the morning and put the kettle on for a cup of tea, washing your sprouts will fit in nicely while you wait for the kettle to boil. It is a two minute job, easy to slot into your life but try where possible to do the same thing every day.

5 Harvest as soon as they are ready – there is a tendency among new sprouters that once the seeds or beans have sprouted, to leave them sitting in their sprouting apparatus to be admired. This is not a good idea. Just like any vegetable or salad stuff which you grow in your garden in a conventional manner, there comes a point when harvesting is essential. So it is with sprouts. When the 'sprouting tail' reaches half an inch on beans and when the first set of green leaves appears on the seeds, then it is time to harvest. If you allow either beans or seeds to sprout for too long, they lose their nutritional value and in many instances their sweetness of taste. Also, when a sprouting

seed turns into a young plant it needs to be sustained in earth for proper growth. Left as a sprout, it becomes a plant under stress, putting all its energy into trying to establish unsatisfactory growth and stay alive. Remember what you are eating is a sprouted seed – a seed not a plant.

6 When your seeds or beans are ready to harvest, always store them covered in the fridge. Beans are particularly good tempered about refrigerated storage and will last for up to a week. Seeds vary but are usually perfectly happy for four or five days which means you can start your new crop and always have fresh food available.

7 Good hygiene is essential for sprouting. Keep all your equipment well washed in hot water to avoid bugs developing.

Sprouting Apparatus

The Jar

For busy people in a family of four, or less, my personal view is the jar is the quickest and easiest method of sprouting. It is almost impossible to mess up sprouting in a jar. It takes up little room and the very minimum of time.

Ideally you should buy a sprouting jar from a health food shop. The alternative is to use a wide necked jar with a piece of muslin over the top but this can prove very messy and it is difficult to drain the seeds properly – undrained seeds lead to rot. Buying a commercial jar is never a waste of money because even if you go on to bigger and better apparatus, you will still need something to soak your seeds in initially and a jar which can be so easily drained is the very best method. For most people I recommend one jar for seeds and another jar for beans.

Method

Most commercial sprouting jars are the equivalent in size of an old fashioned two pound jam jar. Assuming this is the sort of size you are using, place in the jar either a dessertspoon of seeds or two tablespoons of beans. Fill the jar with cold water and soak for the time prescribed in Chapters 2 and 3. If you are soaking either a seed or bean not mentioned in this book, as a general rule of thumb, beans should be soaked overnight for up to twelve hours and seeds usually need four to five hours.

There is a conflict as to the water you use. In an ideal world you should use rain water for your seeds and beans because it is pure with none of the additives found in tap water. However, it is difficult to collect and store sufficient rain water. In addition, when it comes to the washing stage, seeds do benefit from vigorous washing – ie from a tap with a brisk flow. Therefore, what I would recommend, if possible, is that you use rain water for this initial soaking period and tap water for washing thereafter. For extra nutrition at the point of soaking, you can add to the soaking seeds a quarter teaspoon of kelp or wheatgrass powder, but this is absolutely not necessary.

When the soaking time is complete, drain out the water and then vigorously wash the seeds. Assuming you have a commercial jar, just turn on the tap for about a minute and let the water fill the jar and overflow until the water is running clean and clear. Then give the jar a good shake to free the seeds from one another, and drain.

Thereafter, nothing could be more simple. Just once a day, fill the jar again, allow rinsing for about a minute, then drain. If the weather is particularly hot or you are forced to keep your jar somewhere much warmer than normal, you might need to rinse twice a day, but the weather does have to be quite extreme for this to be necessary.

On average, beans will be ready to eat within two days, seeds within five. As soon as they have sprouted, tip them out of the jar, store in the fridge and start your next crop.

The Tray

You can perfectly well sprout seeds in normal plastic seed trays which you can buy from any garden centre. This does not apply to beans, they would dry out too much if sprouted in a tray. For seeds such as alfalfa, red clover, white radish, etc, this method can work very well. Because the seeds are small, it will be necessary for you to cover the bottom of the tray to avoid the seeds dropping through the drainage holes. When I use this method, I line the bottom of the seed tray with organic fleece which is available from most decent garden centres.

Method

You will still need to soak your seeds before putting them on a tray. This is why a jar is always so useful in your life because the mesh at the top of the jar allows water to pass out without taking with it even the smallest seed. Most commercial kitchen sieves have too wide a gauge for small seeds such as alfalfa. If you do not have a jar, then soak your seeds in any container with a lid and place a layer of muslin if you have it, kitchen towel, if not, in the bottom of your sieve when draining the seeds. This is not entirely satisfactory because the whole thing tends to end up fairly messy, but it is the best I can offer if you do not have a jar. A seed tray obviously caters for a much larger quantity of sprouts than a jar. While you cannot successfully grow more than a dessertspoon of seed in a conventional sprouting jar, you can soak up to six dessertspoons in a two pound jar, provided you then transfer the seeds into some other apparatus. Six dessertspoons is about the right amount of seed for a normal seed tray.

Having soaked the seed for the prescribed time, drain and sprinkle it onto the base of the tray on which any fleece or lining should already have been thoroughly dampened. Watering sprouting seeds in a tray is not that easy unless you have a watering can with a fine rose. Turning the tap on will send the seeds scattering in all directions. Alternatively, for just a few pence, you can buy a mist spray from a garden centre. Because the trays are open to the elements, they do dry out much more quickly than the jar. For this reason you will need to spray the seeds at least twice a day, and in hot weather, three times. Once the first set of green leaves have appeared, harvest immediately.

The Bucket

Big beans such as mung, chickpeas, aduki and even lentils do not need any special apparatus at all – just a bucket with a lid, a food container, anything will do, provided you can cover it.

Method

Place a couple of tablespoons (for a family of four) in your bucket and soak for twelve hours. Here again, if you can use rainwater for this initial soaking it is a good idea, and a quarter teaspoon of kelp or wheatgrass powder will add to the nutritional value of the beans though again, this is not necessary. After the soaking time, because the beans are so large, you can rinse them through an ordinary kitchen colander. Keep the water flowing through the beans until it becomes clear. Allow them to thoroughly drain, shaking off any excess water, and then return them to the bucket. Cover but do not make them airtight. If you are using a food container, pierce the lid with a few holes so that the beans can breathe.

You can leave the bucket pretty much anywhere. The concept that beans need to be put in the airing cupboard is completely wrong and they are likely to overheat and become very smelly. Somewhere in the kitchen is ideal, out of the way of direct heat. Once a day return the beans to the colander and thoroughly wash them, wash out the container and then return them again always being careful to drain them thoroughly. After a couple of days the beans will sprout. As soon as they have sprouted, transfer them to the fridge, which will halt the sprouting process, and start again with your next batch.

The Sprouting Bag

I n some health food shops you can buy a hessian sprouting bag, alternatively you can make your own. The bag is just a simple hessian sack about four to six inches square with a drawstring around the top. Bags can only be used for sprouting beans. As you can imagine, if you tried to sprout seeds in them, the seeds would get lost in among the hessian and would also start to put out roots which would make the whole harvesting process extremely messy and difficult! Beans, however, sprout very nicely in a bag, and, of course, the great advantage is that they are very portable – you can take your sprouting bag on holiday with you!

Method

A s with a jar, the whole process takes place within the bag. Put a dessertspoon of beans into your bag and then immerse bag and beans in a basin of water overnight. Remove from the basin and simply run the tap through the bag until the water comes clear. Then pull the drawstring and hang the bag on a tap or a hook you have handy where it can drip and drain. Once a day immerse the bag in a basin of water for at least two minutes, twirling the contents of the bag as you do so to ensure the beans are not stuck together. Then hook the bag up again and allow it to drain. After two to three days, your beans will sprout and, as with other methods, should be harvested and put in the fridge. Turn your bag inside out and thoroughly wash it in hot clear water and it will be ready to use again. It's as simple as that!

The Basket

I n almost any kitchenware shop you can buy cheap imported baskets of various shapes and sizes and provided these have a small tight mesh, they are a very effective and attractive way of growing sprouting seeds. Beans do not work well in baskets as they dry out too quickly. For best results use bamboo baskets, ideally a basket of eight or nine inches in diameter and about two inches in depth is about the right size for the average family of four.

Method

Y ou will need to soak the seeds for the prescribed time and then carefully sprinkle them in the base of the basket and lightly spray seeds and basket once the seeds are in situ. When I grow seeds in a basket, I always put the whole basket in a carrier bag for the first twelve hours to create a mini eco system and prevent the seeds from drying out too quickly. Thereafter, they need to be watered twice a day, or three times in really hot weather, just like the seed trays.

It is important to harvest the sprouting seeds before they get too established in the basket. Because they look attractive, there is a temptation to leave them in situ but once the seeds start putting out serious roots, not only is their nutritional value impaired, you will have the devil of a job trying to clean the basket after use. Try, therefore, to keep your seeds free flowing within the basket.

Commercial Sprouting Trays

There are a number of sprouting trays on the market, usually three tier with a fourth tray to collect water at the bottom. They are made of plastic and either have drainage slits in each tray or drainage valves. If you are wanting to make sprouting part of your everyday life, then these commercial trays are a good idea because they enable you to produce the maximum amount of sprouted seeds and beans in the minimum space.

Some trays are better than others. I personally do not favour the trays with valves which tend to become clogged up with seed in the early stages of sprouting. In fact, for me, the simpler the drainage system the better. I have also found, after surveying what is available in the market place, that those seed trays which are open to fresh air are infinitely preferable to the closed version with a lid. It makes no sense to shut out the air from seed trays and it leads to mould problems.

Method

As with all the sprouting apparatus, seeds and beans have to be soaked first before putting them on the trays. It is best to put beans on the bottom tray as they need the least light and will dry out less easily. Seeds on the top two trays can be rotated so each gets a turn of full light. While the trays do require a degree of preparation initially, if you are wanting to grow several different types of sprouts at once, the actual watering process is very easy. Once a day, you simply pour a mug of water over the top layer and let it filter down through the other layers. As with all sprouting methods, if the weather is extremely hot you may need to do this more often.

Of course, all the trays do not need to be harvested at the same time, so once you have your trays up and running, you can establish a rotation that suits you which will ensure plenty of fresh sprouts for you and your family. So effective are these trays in producing large quantities of sprouts, you may find that you have a glut. Always remember that if you are faced with too many sprouts at any time, don't waste them, juice them!

Sprouting Gelatinous Seeds

Two seeds in particular, which are extremely nutritious but difficult to grow, are flax and sesame. This is because they are gelatinous in consistency when soaked and turn into a sort of goo. The goo, in turn, makes it difficult for the seeds to sprout and the whole thing can end up a very smelly mess. The best way to overcome this is to mix flax and sesame with other seeds which are good tempered and easy to grow – in particular I am thinking of alfalfa and red clover. Whatever method you are intending to use to sprout the seeds, do so on the basis of, say, four alfalfa to one flax. This mix of seeds reduces the gelatinous content and enables both seeds to sprout well. The slight complication is that the soaking times are different. While alfalfa and red clover require 4–6 hours, flax and sesame should only be soaked for ten minutes. You will need to soak the seeds independently of one another and then combine them for sprouting.

Chapter 6
Sprout Health (and harvesting)

I t is easy to tell the difference between a healthy sprout and one in trouble. If the growth on your sprouting seeds is limp or vaguely mushy then, sadly, no amount of coaxing can reverse the problem – they need to be chucked. Healthy sprouts are springy to the touch – you can almost feel the energy and vigour in them. The most reliable detection apparatus, so far as unhealthy sprouts is concerned, is your nose! Sometime before the sprouts actually look awful, they start to smell awful. Assuming you have been washing your sprouts daily and keeping them at a reasonably mild temperature – i.e. not a boiling hot greenhouse, then the most likely reason for unhealthy sprouts is that you have simply left them for too long. There is a tendency among people new to sprouting to leave their seeds or beans malingering in their sprouting equipment. Once sprouted, eat them or refrigerate them. Don't leave them hanging around!

All beans refrigerate really well. As mentioned in previous chapters, do not let the 'tail' on your bean grow longer than half an inch (12mm) for maximum nutrition. Once this is achieved, refrigerate and growth will stop. Provided the bean is young and healthy when it goes into the refrigerator, it should last for a week. Seeds are more volatile and after several days in the fridge, can start to wilt. This is particularly so if the sprouting seeds go into the fridge wet. It is a delicate balance, you don't want the sprouts dried out too much but wet seeds sitting in the fridge tend to go mushy.

For optimum nutritional value, sprouts are best eaten straight from the sprouter and for this reason, rotating small crops is far more satisfactory than growing too much and trying to store it for any length of time. All forms of agriculture thrive on routine and as a sprouter, you are embarking on a career as a mini farmer. A properly established routine is far more likely to make you a successful sprouter and only involves you in two to three minutes a day. Best sprouting practice suggests that you should start off two batches a week. Most sprouting seeds and beans take between two and four days to sprout and are happy in the fridge for about the same period, twice weekly sowing will ensure that you have fresh food all the time.

Mould

Mould is the sprouter's enemy but it is reversible. Particularly in the first day or two of sprouting, there is a tendency for a white mould to develop – a sort of fuzz – on the growing seed. This mould is not at all harmful but what it does indicate is that you are not washing your sprouts either long enough or vigorously enough. As soon as you see the mould develop, up the pressure on your watering and you will see that it disappears immediately it is sprayed. Usually, once the seed is slightly more mature, the mould will disappear completely. Very occasionally a sort of darker, greyer mould appears. This is not good and indicates a bug in your sprouting equipment.

If a dark mould appears, discard the batch of sprouts and sterilise your equipment.

A word on hygiene – where sprouting is concerned cleanliness is really next to godliness. Thoroughly wash your sprouting equipment in piping hot water (I use a little eco friendly washing up liquid) and now and again it is sensible to sterilise everything in the dishwasher. Because you are not dealing with a volatile product, such as meat or dairy, there is a tendency to be rather slapdash with vegetable matter. Sprouts can harbour bacteria like anything else and the cleaner you keep your equipment, the better will be your results.

Husks

During the sprouting process, the husks of the seed are usually discarded. There is no harm in eating them and in fact some of them are quite tasty roughage and contain minerals such as calcium and phosphorous. However, for sprout health, it is good to remove husks if you are intending to store your sprouts for any length of time. If you put your beans or seeds in a colander and then immerse the colander in a bowl of water, the husks will float to the surface. By using a slatted spoon, you can simply remove the husks by skimming them off the surface of the water. This is not an exact science, you are not trying to remove every single one, but the less clogged up your sprouts, the healthier they will be. A good example is mung beans. Mung beans seem to shed their shell far more vigorously than other beans. While it is perfectly alright to eat these bits of green shell they are not specially attractive and do stop air circulating around the rest of the bean. By following the method just described, the husks can be removed easily.

Poor health in sprouts is so often linked to over-production. It is very easy to over produce with the result that you start eating sprouts when they are not at their best and most nutritious. One way around this is to juice them. Throwing a handful of sprouted seeds or beans into your juicer along with some fruit and vegetables is a good way to take your daily dose of sprouts. I always recommend this method for people who are requiring to take a large quantity of sprouts because of ill health and who have become tired of chomping their way through salad after salad. So if you find yourself having produced a glut of a particular sprout, don't keep it too long – juice it!

So, routine is the key to successful sprouting. Synchronising how much you grow with how much you eat will ensure you eat sprouts at their very best and most nutritious. With regular washing and careful hygiene, you really cannot fail. As an added bonus, most sprouters find it a deeply satisfying experience to be producing their own food.

Chapter 7
Your Health

Working in a shop daily, as I do, talking to people about their nutritional needs and health problems, there are two buzz words which recur again and again during discussions. These are: energy and stress.

Energy
(or rather the lack of it)

Understandably, it is sometimes quite difficult to persuade people in a shop environment to talk about their health problems. However, the moment you mention the energising quality of a seed or bean, people immediately open up. 'That's what I need!', they cry. It appears to be a national disease – everyone is tired and lacking the energy to do anything other than work and care for themselves and their family, dragging themselves around, longing to collapse in a heap. This is not because we have become a lazy nation, far from it, we work a great deal harder than most of Europe, packing more into our day. The problem lies in the quality of the food we eat. It is fuel of a sort, satisfying the hunger pangs, giving us a 'full up' feeling but it is the quality of the fuel which is the problem. Recent scientific surveys have shown that the nutritional value of food has dropped by 80% – yes, 80% – since 1988, and 1988 was not a very good starting point. This huge drop is attributed to a combination of the way our food is grown and the way it is distributed to the retailer. Our bodies are constantly under stress because of poor nutrition. We are forcing them to perform without giving them the tools to do the job. No wonder we feel so tired.

It is so ironic that while obesity is terrifyingly on the increase, many people, even including some who are obese, are in fact malnourished. My generation, who grew up in the Fifties, were so lucky. My family had a kitchen garden, a few hens scratching around to provide our eggs, our milk came from the dairy of a local farmer, our butcher sourced all his meat locally, because it would never have occurred to him to do anything else, and my mother baked. When I look back on it now, it is absolutely extraordinary the amount of food we ate. Breakfast always consisted of porridge, some sort of eggs, toast and fruit. When I was home from school there was always elevenses – a drink and a slice of home made cake. Lunch was always two courses, which included a pudding, and then there was afternoon tea with sandwiches, more cake, followed by a supper meal for children and dinner, later, for parents. Were we fat? Not at all. It is true that our life was less sedentary than it is today but mostly it was about the quality of the food - fresh ingredients, no additives, nothing processed. Sadly we cannot turn back to the nutritional climate of the Fifties - those days have gone forever. However, energy levels can be dramatically improved by the daily eating of fresh young sprouts. An undernourished body cannot be expected to perform properly, but you do have the ability to put it right.

Stress

Ask any one of the customers who visit my shop if their health problems are due to stress, and the answer is invariably, yes. While the media fuss about SARS and bird flu, they are overlooking the most chronic plague to sweep the Western world, which – while no one was looking – has crept in the back door. Stress is a killer. It causes the sufferer to be more susceptible to heart disease, strokes, cancer and a whole range of chronic illnesses. It also takes years off normal life expectancy.

In addition, long-term stress plays havoc with the hormones. The body is intended to be in a heightened state of alert just occasionally in order to deal with the odd crisis which may occur during the average day. However, when you spend most of your life in a state of stress, then your poor old body stays in that heightened state of alert, with adrenaline pumping around it, all the time. Your hormones then become confused and cannot return to their normal state, even when, say, at the weekend, your stress level drops. The resulting chaos increases your blood sugar which in turn causes chronic fatigue, high blood pressure and even weight gain. Your body simply wasn't built to be stressed out all the time.

When stressed, sadly, the natural props one leans towards to find relief only make things worse – a cup of coffee to calm you down after a particularly fraught journey into work actually encourages the release of adrenaline and therefore increases levels of stress, not reduces them. Diving into the nearest pub or wine bar after a heavy day, seeking a drink or two to chill out, again has the reverse effect. Alcohol stimulates secretion of adrenaline and makes matters worse. Equally, comfort food is counter productive. You buy a chocolate bar at the motorway services when you fill up with petrol. It is useful to help you keep awake, but will do nothing at all for your stress levels when you are confronted with yet another set of road works. It is an ironic situation that the traditional props to which we are drawn to help us unwind only serve to increase the problem.

It is often said that stress is actually good for people, but it is important not to confuse stress with stimulation. Keeping active, physically and mentally, is absolutely essential for good health, and finding oneself in a testing situation from time to time is equally so. What I am talking about is these prolonged periods of heightened stress which lead to being permanently tired, bad tempered, depressed, jumpy, restless and often suffering from insomnia.

If this is you then you need to do something about it – fast. Eating several helpings of sprouts a day is not, of course, a cure all – if only it were that simple! However, I don't think it is fair to ask people to start changing their lives in an effort to 'de-stress' until their bodies are taking in the right fuel to provide the energy they need to cope with their day. Eating in a way which will rapidly increase your energy levels could be enough in itself to combat stress, particularly where your stress is linked to not coping. I list overleaf the foods which are good to avoid and those upon which you should concentrate when very stressed.

Bad foods

Alcohol
Caffeine
Red Meat
Refined and processed food
Dairy products
Salty foods
Sweets and sugary foods
Additives, preservatives and pesticides
– in other words avoid non-organic food.

Good foods

All fruits but particularly berries
All vegetables, particularly celery, asparagus, cucumber,
cabbage and garlic
Brown rice and pasta
White meat
Fish
Pulses
Two big helpings of sprouts a day!

Sprouting and weight control

I may be an old misery, but I do not approve of diets.
Some are better than others, of course, and some are
more attractive to follow than others, but they all end up
the same in the end – while you are on your diet you lose
weight, when you stop, you go back to where you were
before you started – all very depressing!

If we are overweight, it is because we are eating the wrong

food and no meaningful results are going to be achieved by simply eating less of the wrong food. What you have to do is to find a formula for living and eating healthily, and your weight will then fall off naturally and permanently. Trying to stick to a rigid diet is soul-destroying – you find yourself eating something you know you shouldn't and feel guilty while you do it, so it brings you no pleasure, so why did you do it in the first place – it is all such a negative experience. In broad terms, you want to eat food which is high in nutritional value and energy and, by definition, such foods are low in fat and other potential weight gain factors.

The control centre in charge of our appetite is very confused these days. We eat so much rubbish that the body no longer knows whether we have eaten enough or not. If we continue to eat rubbish, but just less of it – in an attempt to lose weight – we will become absolutely exhausted in just a few days, particularly if we embark on an exercise programme as well. It is the exhaustion factor which so often defeats would-be dieters. The good and bad foods I outlined for combating stress are equally relevant for weight loss. They are the staple foods upon which to build a healthy mind and body. If you eat only fruits, vegetables, unprocessed foods, unrefined rice, pasta etc, etc, weight loss will follow, and this is where sprouts come in very handy.

The layers of fat we lay down around our bodies are used to store toxic residues. It is an unpleasant thought but basically, they are the body's dustbin for those grizzly toxins that our system is unable to dispose of in any other way. As we start to eat better then we will also start to burn off these fat deposits, which we have probably been carrying around for some years. As this happens, the toxins get dumped into the blood stream and this is what causes the unpleasant 'detox symptoms' – ie headaches, flu like feelings, all very nasty. How quickly we can get over this period depends to a large extent on what we eat. The toxins being released into the bloodstream are acidic and therefore we need to be eating alkaline foods. All sprouts are alkaline-forming and therefore the perfect food during any detox programme to help maintain energy and reduce symptoms. They are also a good source of fibre, which contributes to the elimination of unwanted substances and they provide vital energy at a time when our body is trying to adjust to new healthy eating.

DON'T DIET, JUST CHANGE YOUR EATING HABITS

The Immune System

The human immune system is truly wonderful and actually requires very little from us to function properly. It needs good quality food, sleep, fresh clean water and unpolluted air. Given these things and it will always be ahead of the game – beating off bacteria, viruses, carcinogenic cells, allergies and the ever increasing new diseases we seem to be getting so good at producing, such as ME and, of course, the horror of AIDS. Our immune systems are desperate for help.

The early human diet in an unpolluted world consisted mainly of nuts, seeds, fruits and baby sprouting seeds. There was no meat, no dairy products, no processed food. Unable to cook, our ancestors lived on a raw, vegetarian diet. They must have been a very healthy species indeed, a million years ago, and we should try to emulate them. Boosting the immune system means putting anti-oxidants into your body in quick absorbable form – wheatgrass juice is perfect so are sprouted broccoli and alfalfa – but all sprouting seeds and beans have a major contribution to make.

Chronic Illness

I t is widely recognised that the high concentration of anti-oxidant nutrients in sprouting seeds and beans, fight against the damage caused by free radicals. Free radicals are those nasty things produced within our bodies which cause cell damage and accelerate the ageing process – cell damage, of course, can lead to cancer. A team of researchers at the University of Texas Cancer Center have been experimenting with sprouted seeds, mostly broccoli. They found that cancer cells were 'ninety nine percent inhibited' by feeding their patients live broccoli sprouts. It has been discovered that broccoli contains glucoraphanin, a chemical that, when eaten, is converted by the body into sulforaphane which is the strongest natural inducer of the body's own enzymes against carcinogens. According to Paul Talalay, PhD, a pharmacologist at the John Hopkins University: 'In animal and human cells, we have demonstrated, unequivocally, that this compound can substantially reduce the incident rate of development and size of tumours.' Scientists found that broccoli sprouts contained a concentration of glucoraphanin that is up to fifty times greater than the mature broccoli we buy as a vegetable. It is impressive stuff. No one is suggesting that eating large quantities of broccoli sprouts will cure cancer, particularly at an advanced stage, but it will help and its role as a preventative is without question.

Cancer is the scourge in today's world, so is heart disease and the spin off from the environment in which we live is high cholesterol, high blood pressure and liver damage. A move towards eating raw foods, the introduction of sprouting seeds, beans and wheatgrass juice into your diet is the best possible thing you can do to keep yourself healthy. All you have to do is to try it because once you have, you won't need any further persuasion from me. The introduction of these fabulous superfoods into your life will alter the way you feel, not in months, nor in weeks, but in just a few days. They speak for themselves.

Chapter 9
Sprouting Recipes

I am often asked by customers what to do with sprouts once they have grown them. The quickest and easiest way to eat them, of course, is to simply munch them as a finger food – they are delicious – but I do appreciate that it is good to ring the changes and also find ways of introducing them to the rest of your family and friends.

The recipes in this book are very individual and very much mine, so they are rather a hotchpotch of ideas. However they are ideas that work and are also regularly eaten by my children – no small consideration given that they are a bunch of teenagers who are at an age when co-operation with Mother isn't necessarily a given!

I hope you enjoy them and that they inspire you to keep sprouting.

Soups

Courgette Soup

400g (1lb) courgettes, sliced
1 small onion, chopped
1 medium potato, cubed
600ml (1 pint) light stock
100g (4oz) mung bean sprouts
25g (1oz) broccoli sprouts
1 tablespoon olive oil
salt and pepper
parsley, chopped (for garnish)

Soften the onion in the oil but do not brown, add courgettes and potato. Coat with oil and then add the stock. Simmer gently until the vegetables are soft. Put in a blender with the mung bean and broccoli sprouts. Add seasoning to taste (no salt necessary if using a stock cube). Garnish with parsley before serving.

Soups

Tangy Tomato Soup

800g (2lb) tomatoes, quartered
1 large onion, chopped
1 potato, cubed
2 tablespoons olive oil
1.2 litres (2 pints) vegetable stock
50g (2oz) white radish sprouts
50g (2oz) red clover sprouts
100g (4oz) brown lentil sprouts
salt and pepper
soured cream to serve

Soften onion in oil. Add potato, tomatoes and stock. Simmer gently until potatoes are soft. Blend with all the sprouts. Add salt and pepper to taste. Serve with a dollop of soured cream in each bowl.

Soups

Lettuce Soup

1 large lettuce
200g (8oz) potatoes, peeled and cubed
1 onion, chopped
2 tablespoons olive oil
100g (4oz) alfalfa
100g (4oz) sprouted mung beans
600ml (1 pint) light vegetable stock
salt and pepper
chopped chives or parsley for garnish

Soften onion in oil and then add potatoes. Toss in the oil and then add the vegetable stock. Simmer gently until potatoes are soft. Shred the lettuce and add to the pan. Continue cooking to wilt the lettuce. Add the mung and alfalfa and then blend in a food processor or using a hand-held blender. Season to taste. Garnish with chives or parsley.

Cold Soups

Cucumber and Avocado Soup

3 small or 2 large cucumbers
2 ripe avocados
1 clove garlic, crushed (optional)
juice of 1 lemon
50g (2oz) broccoli sprouts
50g (2oz) white radish sprouts
25g (1oz) alfalfa
mint leaves
200g (8oz) natural yoghurt
chopped chives to garnish

Chop cucumber and avocados roughly. Place all the ingredients in a large bowl or food processor and blend until smooth. Adjust seasoning. Chill in refrigerator and garnish with chopped chives before serving.

Cold Soups

Gazpacho

1 small or ¾ large cucumber, chopped
400g (1lb) tomatoes, quartered
1 red and green pepper, chopped
1 medium onion, chopped
75g (3oz) red clover sprouts
50g (2oz) broccoli sprouts
2 cloves garlic, crushed
4 tablespoons extra virgin olive oil
1 tablespoon balsamic vinegar
450ml (¾ pint) water
150ml (¼ pint) tomato juice
salt and pepper
bunch of chopped mixed basil and parsley
or small croutons to garnish

Combine all the ingredients (except the basil and parsley or croutons and salt and pepper) in a large bowl. Blend with a hand-hand blender (or put everything in a large food processor). Add salt and pepper as necessary. Chill in the refrigerator (overnight if possible). Sprinkle with garnish of choice before serving.

Pasta

Quick Pasta Snack

150g (6oz) *light pasta*
200g (8oz) *natural yoghurt*
1 *clove of garlic, crushed*
100g (4oz) *mixed sprouted beans and/or lentils*
(ie mung, aduki, chickpea and brown lentils)
25g (1oz) *fenugreek sprouts*
25g (1oz) *red clove sprouts*
salt and pepper to taste

Cook the pasta in plenty of boiling water. Meanwhile combine all the other ingredients and warm gently. Pour over the cooked and drained pasta. Serve immediately.

Pasta

Green and Yellow Pasta

200g (8oz) pasta
1 avocado
50g (2oz) fenugreek sprouts
50g (2oz) alfalfa
75g (3oz) mung bean sprouts
2 spring onions, sliced
1 green and 1 yellow pepper
small tin sweetcorn (drained) or equivalent frozen
2 tablespoons olive oil (reserving a little for the pasta – see below)
salt and pepper

Heat oil and add peppers. Fry gently until soft. Add spring onions and mix. Continue to fry for a few more minutes and then add everything else except the pasta. Stir well and heat through. Adjust seasoning to taste. Meanwhile cook the pasta. Drain and toss in a little olive oil then stir in the prepared vegetables and sprouts. Serve immediately.

Pasta

Pasta with Goats' Cheese
and Roasted Vegetables

200g (8oz) wholemeal pasta
100g (4oz) creamy goats' cheese
1 red, green and yellow pepper, chopped
1 red onion, chopped
olive oil
2 cloves garlic, crushed
50g (2oz) fenugreek sprouts
25g (1oz) white radish sprouts
25g (1oz) broccoli sprouts
salt and pepper to taste

Toss peppers, garlic and onion in oil and place on a baking tray. Bake in a hot oven 200C/400F/Gas Mark 6 until soft (approximately 20–25 minutes). Transfer into a casserole dish and add the chopped goats' cheese and the sprouts. Season to taste. Cover and place in a moderate over to heat through whilst cooking the pasta. Combine and serve immediately.

Main meals

Chicken Breasts with Cream Sauce

4 chicken breasts
75g (3oz) grapes
50g (2oz) alfalfa sprouts
50g (2oz) broccoli sprouts
25g (1oz) butter
25g (1oz) olive oil
tarragon (optional)
juice of 1 lemon
white wine (optional)

Sauce

35g (1½oz) butter
25g (1oz) plain flour
300ml (½ pint) juice from cooked
chicken with added milk as
necessary
salt and pepper to taste

Melt the oil and butter in a baking dish. Add the chicken, tarragon (optional), wine (optional) and lemon juice. Cover with a lid or foil and cook in a moderate oven 175C/380F/ Gas Mark 5 until chicken is tender (approximately ½ hour). Place chicken on a warm serving dish and keep warm whilst making the sauce using the juices from the chicken. Make sauce by melting butter, stirring in flour and then blending in liquid. Check seasoning and add salt and pepper to taste. Mix in grapes (peeled if preferred) and the sprouts. Reheat and pour immediately over the chicken.

Main Meals

Salmon Bake

4 salmon steaks
2 spring onions
knob of butter
juice of 1 lemon
50g (2oz) mung bean sprouts
25g (1oz) broccoli sprouts
25g (1oz) alfalfa
salt and pepper to taste
chopped parsley to garnish

Melt the butter in a baking dish. Put all the ingredients except the sprouts into the dish and cover tightly. Place in oven 200C/400F/Gas Mark 6 until the fish is tender (approximately 20–25 minutes). When the fish is cooked, stir in the sprouts and return to the oven to warm (approximately 5 minutes). Serve with chopped parsley.

Main Meals

Chick Pea Casserole

200g (8oz) chick pea sprouts
400g (1lb) tomatoes, quartered
1 large onion, roughly chopped
1 red and green pepper, sliced
100g (4oz) mushrooms, quartered
200g (8oz) courgettes, sliced
100g (4oz) white radish sprouts
25g (1oz) fenugreek sprouts
2 tblsps olive oil
salt and pepper

Soften the onion in the oil. Add the peppers, mix well and continue to cook for another 5 minutes. Add the tomatoes, courgettes and mushrooms. Stir in the chick peas. Cook in a moderate oven 180C/360F/Gas Mark 4 for ½ hour. Immediately before serving, stir in the fenugreek and white radish and check seasoning.

Main Meals

Sprouting Burger

100g (4oz) sprouted chick peas
½ jar of tahini
50g (2oz) sunflower seeds
100g (4oz) sprouted aduki beans
1 dessertspoon sesame seeds
5–6 tablespoons miso
2 cloves garlic, crushed (optional)
1 large onion, finely chopped
1 tablespoon Hungarian paprika
1 dessertspoon chopped coriander and marjoram
(or 1 teaspoon dried mixed herbs)

Mix all the ingredients in a food processor. If the mixture is too firm to shape into burgers, add some sesame or brazil oil. If too moist, you could add a few soft breadcrumbs or ground almonds. Shape into burgers and place on an oiled baking tray. Bake at 200C/400F/Gas Mark 6 until brown (approximately 10 minutes on each side).

Main Meals

Baked Cod with Tomatoes and Sprouts

Cod fillets
1 onion, sliced
1 clove garlic, crushed
200g (8oz) tomatoes, sliced
2 tablespoons fenugreek sprouts
2 tablespoons red clover sprouts
juice of 1 lemon
1 tablespoon olive oil
25g (1oz) butter

Soften the onion in oil and butter mixture and add the garlic. Remove from heat. Put fish on top of onion and garlic. Spread with tomatoes. Pour over lemon juice and salt and pepper to taste. Cover tightly and cook in oven at 200C/400F/Gas Mark 6 for about 25 minutes. Cooking time will vary according to the thickness of the fillets. Stir in the sprouts. Cover and return to the oven for a few minutes to warm the sprouts.

Main Meals

Risotto

200g (8oz) brown rice
450ml (¾ pint) water (approx)
1 large onion, chopped
2 tablespoons olive oil
1 read and green pepper, chopped
100g (4oz) mushrooms, sliced
200g (8oz) cherry tomatoes, halved
50g (2oz) broccoli sprouts
50g (2oz) fenugreek sprouts
100g (4oz) aduki bean sprouts
75g (3oz) cheddar cheese and 25g (1oz) parmesan (or 100g (4oz) cheddar), grated
salt and pepper to taste

Soften onion in oil and add the washed rice. Coat in oil and add water and simmer until all the water is absorbed and the rice is cooked. Check during cooking and add more water if necessary. Meanwhile, in a large frying pan, fry red and green peppers until softened. Add mushrooms and tomatoes and continue cooking for 10 minutes. Stir in the sprouted seeds and beans. Add a handful of sunflower seeds. Combine with the cooked rice and adjust seasoning. Top with the grated cheese and melt under the grill.

Main Meals

Sprout and Vegetable Stew

3 cups of mixed sprouts
2 cups of diced carrots
1 cup of diced beetroot
3 large stalks of celery, finely sliced
1 onion, chopped finely
4 large tomatoes or a tin of chopped tomatoes
2 courgettes, finely chopped
1 small bunch of chopped coriander
300ml (½ pint) vegetable stock
salt and pepper
2 tablespoons of flour
1 chilli (optional)

Fry the onion, spices and herbs together in a little oil or butter. Add flour and make a rue. Add 300ml (½ pint) of vegetable stock and all the ingredients except the sprouts. Mix in well and put in a medium oven for 15 minutes. Remove from oven and fold in the sprouts. Serve immediately with crunchy French bread.

Salads

Beetroot and Sunflower
(or flax) Seed Sprout Salad

100g (4oz) sunflower (or flax) seed sprouts
200g (8oz) beetroot, grated
100g (4oz) mushrooms, sliced thinly
50g (2oz) sprouted mung beans
handful of parsley or coriander, chopped (if available)

Vinaigrette dressing

1 clove garlic, crushed
pinch of salt
½ teaspoon dry mustard
6 tablespoons olive oil
2 tablespoons cider vinegar,
ground pepper

Combine all the seeds and vegetables and toss in sufficient dressing to coat the salad. Check seasoning and sprinkle with parsley or coriander, if available.

Salads

Crunchy Salad

200g (8oz) mixed sprouted beans and lentils (eg brown lentils, mung
and aduki beans)
75g (3oz) fenugreek sprouts
1 cucumber, chopped
1 head celery (omit coarse outer sticks)
4 spring onions, sliced

Dressing

50g (2oz) soured cream
50g (2oz) yoghurt
juice of 1 lemon
1 clove crushed garlic
salt and pepper

Salads

Simple and Delicious Green Salad

Mixed salad leaves
1 avocado, chopped
100g (4oz) mung bean sprouts
75g (3oz) alfalfa
50g (2oz) broccoli sprouts

Dressing

Simple vinaigrette using lemon juice rather than vinegar.

Salads

Substantial Salad

100g (4oz) mangetout
100g (4oz) mixed sprouted beans – brown lentils, mung
and aduki beans
1 carrot, grated
50g (2oz) white radish
50g (2oz) alfalfa
25g (1oz) sesame seed sprouts
small cucumber, cubed
small lettuce, shredded
4 tomatoes, quartered
100g (4oz) flaked tuna
100g (4oz) cooked and cubed potatoes.

Dressing

1 clove garlic crushed with a pinch of salt
1 teaspoon dry mustard powder
6 tablespoons brazil nut oil
2 tablespoons cider vinegar

Salads

Potato Salad

2 cups of sprouted mung beans
4 medium potatoes, boiled
1 cup of mayonnaise
½ cup of yoghurt
chives or diced spring onions

Cube the potatoes and slice the leek. Mix together the mayonnaise and the yoghurt and add the chives. Pour over the potatoes and leek and mix in the sprouting mung beans. Garnish with a few extra chives.

Canapes

Lettuce Leaf Wrap

Large lettuce leaves (Webb's would be good)
1 carrot, grated
1 yellow pepper, finely chopped
50g (2oz) sprouted aduki beans
50g (2oz) sprouted mung beans
25g (1oz) white radish
25g (1oz) alfalfa
juice of 1 lemon
hempseed butter or cashew nut butter
brazil nut oil or sesame seed oil

Dip

150ml (¼ pint) soured cream
1 tablespoon cider vinegar
small clove garlic

Place all the vegetables and sprouts in a bowl. Combine with the chosen butter and a little oil to make a suitable consistency to hold together. Spoon on to the lettuce leaves. Wrap and secure with a cocktail stick.

Canapes

Sushi Rolls

Sushi sheets
100g (4oz) brown rice
200ml (7 fl oz) good quality
vegetable stock
2 ripe avocados
1 carrot, grated
1 large (or 2 small) spring onion
50g (2oz) mung bean sprouts
25g (1oz) red clover sprouts
25g (1oz) fenugreek sprouts
25g (1oz) alfalfa
juice of 1 lemon

Piquant Dressing

6 tablespoons olive oil or brazil
nut oil
3 tablespoons cider vinegar
1 teaspoon soy sauce
1 teaspoon muscovado sugar
½ teaspoon Hungarian paprika
chopped chives
salt and pepper

Cook the rice in the stock. All the water should be absorbed. Mix all the ingredients. Moisten with extra lemon juice if necessary to make a homogeneous mass. Check seasoning. Spread on sushi sheets and roll, wrapping in ends. Moisten the top edges with water to make them stick. Chill in the refrigerator until required. Serve with a suitable dressing for dipping such as the piquant dressing.

Juices

These are just some suggestions to get started.
Try different ingredients and quantities.
The combinations are legion.
Experiment!

Carrot, Celery, Cucumber
100g (4oz) carrot
1 stick celery
a small chunk cucumber
25g (1oz) alfalfa
25g (1oz) broccoli sprouts
25g (1oz) red clover sprouts
1 apple (add if you want a sweeter juice)

Carrot, Apple, Avocado
100g (4oz) carrot
1 medium apple
1 avocado
50g (2oz) alfalfa

Apple. Melon, Carrot

1 apple
25g (1oz) alfalfa
1 slice melon
25mm root ginger
150g (6oz) carrot
25g (1oz) alfalfa
25g (1oz) white radish
25g (1oz) sunflower seed sprouts

A Few Tips

Bread

Try adding alfalfa to your favourite basic bread recipe or, for a more nutty flavour, aduki or mung bean sprouts would be interesting. Flax seed and sesame seed sprouts are also excellent in bread.

Scrambled Eggs with a Difference

Make scrambled eggs in the normal way. Add 1 tablespoon each of white radish and red clover. Serve immediately.

A Nutritious Variant on the ever-popular (and quick) Cauliflower Cheese

Cook cauliflower as usual and make the cheese sauce. Before pouring over the cooked vegetable, stir in chopped red pepper and a handful of mixed sprouting beans (eg mung, aduki, lentil, chick pea). Adjust quantities according to the number of servings.

Sprouts and Vegetables

Sprouts added to boiled, steamed or braised vegetables are delicious. A variety of combinations work well together. Some suggestions:

Carrot and fenugreek
Carrots and alfalfa
Peas and white radish
Peas and alfalfa
Broccoli and mung beans
Broccoli and aduki beans
Broad beans and lentils
Brussel sprouts and mung beans
Cabbage and white radish
Cabbage and red clover
Courgettes and broccoli sprouts
Cauliflower and mung bean
French beans and flax seed

Simply cook the vegetables according to your preferred method and stir in the chosen sprouted seeds or beans immediately prior to serving. There is no need for additional cooking.

Sandwiches

Throughout this book, I have referred to the benefits of sprouts being used in sandwich fillings. I thought it would be helpful, therefore, to provide a few ideas for your consideration.

For high nutritional value, use wholemeal bread or rolls rather than white, and also think in terms of wraps, which are a great alternative to the traditional sandwich and are also available wholemeal.

The fillings I suggest can be used with baked potatoes or served with rice, added to cold pasta, or cooked quinoa. Although a salad sandwich sounds a noble choice – particularly if no fats are involved, such as mayonnaise or butter – a traditional salad has very little nutritional value. Think in terms of adding carrots (raw, of course!), red peppers, tomatoes and watercress because these foods are high in vitamin C and antioxidants. If, in addition, you add a good helping of sprouts, you turn the humble sandwich into a nutritional powerhouse. For protein, think in terms of adding chicken, tuna, egg, cheese or fish – such as salmon or sardines. If you are a vegetarian, aduki beans, in particular, are very high in protein.

Here are a dozen ideas for sandwich fillings to get you going:

1. Grated carrot and alfalfa, bound together with a little mayo, a squeeze of lemon juice and black pepper. You can also add ham to this, if you wish. No butter.

2. Sliced tomato with brown or green lentils. Bind together with a little cream cheese but no butter.

3. Sliced cucumber, mung beans, alfalfa and white radish, again bind with a little cream cheese or mayo. If using mayo, you could add meat, chicken or fish to this combination – Parma ham is particularly good.

4. Grated cheddar cheese with mixed beans (aduki, mung and or lentils). Bind with mayo, add a touch of black pepper.

5. Hummus with mixed beans, lemon juice, a little crushed garlic and black pepper.

6. You can buy some wonderful nut and seed butters. Spread these on your bread or rolls and then add lettuce and alfalfa or mixed beans.

7. Avocado, peeled, stoned and mashed with a little mayo. Add watercress, sliced tomato and alfalfa.

8. Avocado mashed with mayo and added to small slices of chicken and mung beans.

9. Scrape a little marmite on the bread or rolls and add lettuce and alfalfa.

10. Mash together a piece of cooked salmon with mayo, adding a little lemon juice and black pepper. Add fenugreek sprouts.

11. Guacumole dip with red clover and alfalfa added.

12. Black olive tapenade with lettuce and mixed beans.

Of course, there are thousands of possible variations on the above themes. Adding fresh herbs gives flavour and avoids the temptation of using too much seasoning. Introduce pine nuts and unsprouted seeds, such as pumpkin and sunflower, to give texture. Fruit, too, is good; grate apple with carrot (remembering to squeeze a little lemon juice over the apple to stop it going brown); put sliced mango in with white radish; add kiwi to tomato, watercress and alfalfa; add raisins and unsweetened cranberries and blueberries. Experiment, be daring and your sandwiches will not only be nutritious but a positive gourmet experience!

D eborah's shop LIVING FOOD is in St Ives, where you will find a wide choice of organic seeds and beans for sprouting, sprouting equipment and a supporting range of nutricious food and food supplements.

The address is: LIVING FOOD OF ST IVES,
                    PIER HOUSE,
                    5, QUAY STREET,
                    ST IVES,
                    CORNWALL
                    TR26 1PT

(The shop is to be found at the far end of the harbour, by Smeaton's Quay and the lighthouse.)

Opening hours: 10am – 4pm Monday to Friday
                   10am – 5pm Saturday
                   Closed   on Sundays

The shop is open all year round except for the last two weeks of January.

LIVING FOOD offers a FREE mail order service to all UK mainland addresses. You can order online:

www.sproutingseeds.co.uk

or telephone 01736 791981 to place an order or obtain a free brochure.